Grade 1

Treasures

Grammar
PRACTICE BOOK

Macmillan
McGraw-Hill

B

The *McGraw·Hill* Companies

Macmillan
McGraw-Hill

Published by Macmillan/McGraw-Hill, of McGraw-Hill Education, a division of The McGraw-Hill Companies, Inc.,
Two Penn Plaza, New York, New York 10121.

Printed in the United States of America

4 5 6 7 8 9 10 066 09 08 07

Contents

Unit 1 • All About Us

We Are Special
Pam and Sam
Sentences 1
Sentences 2
Mechanics 3
Proofreading 4
Review and Assess 5

Ready, Set, Move!
I Can! Can You?
Word Order 6
Word Order 7
Mechanics 8
Proofreading 9
Review and Assess 10

Growing Up
Time For Kids:
How You Grew
Statements 11
Statements 12
Mechanics 13
Proofreading 14
Review and Assess 15

Pets
Pet Tricks
Questions and Exclamations 16
Questions and Exclamations 17
Mechanics 18
Proofreading 19
Review and Assess 20

Teamwork
Soccer
Writing Sentences 21
Writing Sentences 22
Mechanics 23
Proofreading 24
Review and Assess 25

Unit 2 • Outside My Door

Animal Families
Animal Moms and Dads
Nouns. 26
Nouns. 27
Mechanics. 28
Proofreading 29
Review and Assess. 30

Helping Out
Little Red Hen
Plural Nouns 31
Plural Nouns 32
Mechanics. 33
Proofreading 34
Review and Assess. 35

Where Animals Live
Time For Kids:
A Prairie Dog Home
Irregular Plural Nouns. 36
Irregular Plural Nouns. 37
Mechanics. 38
Proofreading 39
Review and Assess. 40

Sing and Dance!
The Fun Kids' Band
Proper Nouns 41
Proper Nouns 42
Mechanics. 43
Proofreading 44
Review and Assess. 45

Let's Laugh
On My Way to School
Days, Months, and Holidays. 46
Days, Months, and Holidays. 47
Mechanics. 48
Proofreading 49
Review and Assess. 50

Unit 3 • Let's Connect

Being Friends
Kate's Game

Verbs 51
Verbs 52
Mechanics 53
Proofreading 54
Review and Assess 55

Kids Around the World
Kids Can Help

Present Tense Verbs 56
Present Tense Verbs 57
Mechanics 58
Proofreading 59
Review and Assess 60

Me and My Shadow
Time For Kids: Short
Shadows, Long Shadows

Past Tense Verbs 61
Past Tense Verbs 62
Mechanics 63
Proofreading 64
Review and Assess 65

Our Families
Smile Mike!

Is and Are 66
Is and Are 67
Mechanics 68
Proofreading 69
Review and Assess 70

Family Time
Gram and Me

Contractions with *Not* 71
Contractions with *Not* 72
Mechanics 73
Proofreading 74
Review and Assess 75

Unit 4 • Our Earth

Birds
Pelican Was Hungry

Was and Were...76
Was and Were...77
Mechanics..78
Proofreading...79
Review and Assess..80

Recycling
June Robot Cleans Up

Has and Have...81
Has and Have...82
Mechanics..83
Proofreading...84
Review and Assess..85

What's the Weather?
Time For Kids:
Stormy Weather

Go and Do..86
Go and Do..87
Mechanics..88
Proofreading...89
Review and Assess..90

What Scientists Do
Meet Ben Franklin

See and Say..91
See and Say..92
Mechanics..93
Proofreading...94
Review and Assess..95

Favorite Stories
Little Rabbit and the
Falling Fruit

Contractions with *Not*....................................96
Contractions with *Not*....................................97
Mechanics..98
Proofreading...99
Review and Assess...100

Unit 5 • I Can Do It!

Express Yourself
Olivia

Adjectives 101
Adjectives 102
Mechanics 103
Proofreading 104
Review and Assess 105

Watch It Go
Frog and Toad: The Kite

Adjectives That Compare 106
Adjectives That Compare 107
Mechanics 108
Proofreading 109
Review and Assess 110

Inventions
**Time For Kids: Kids'
Great Inventions**

Color Words 111
Color Words 112
Mechanics 113
Proofreading 114
Review and Assess 115

I Can Do It
Whistle for Willie

Number Words 116
Number Words 117
Mechanics 118
Proofreading 119
Review and Assess 120

How Does It Grow?
**A Fruit Is a Suitcase for
Seeds**

Synonyms and Antonyms 121
Synonyms and Antonyms 122
Mechanics 123
Proofreading 124
Review and Assess 125

Unit 6 • Let's Discover

Bugs, Bugs, Bugs!
Dot and Jabber and the Big Bug Mystery

Subjects...126
Subjects...127
Mechanics...128
Proofreading......................................129
Review and Assess................................130

Exploring Space
Little Bear Goes to the Moon

Predicates..131
Predicates..132
Mechanics...133
Proofreading......................................134
Review and Assess................................135

At Work
Time For Kids: Cool Jobs

Pronouns..136
Pronouns..137
Mechanics...138
Proofreading......................................139
Review and Assess................................140

Watching Animals Grow
A Tiger Cub Grows Up

I or Me..141
I or Me..142
Mechanics...143
Proofreading......................................144
Review and Assess................................145

Let's Build
Sand Castle

Combining Sentences..............................146
Combining Sentences..............................147
Mechanics...148
Proofreading......................................149
Review and Assess................................150

Name_____

> A sentence is a group of words that tells a whole idea.
>
> Example: The cat can jump.

Circle the sentences.

1. (She sat down.)

2. (We can jump up.)

3. Ran here.

4. (Pat can do this.)

5. Like to.

© Macmillan/McGraw-Hill

At Home: Make up a sentence about each member of your family.

Pam and Sam • **Book 1.1/Unit 1**   1

Name_____

A sentence is a group of words that tells a whole idea.

Use the words in the box to make sentences.

Pam	can jump	ran down	The hat

1. My cat __can jump__.

2. ___Pam___ has a hat.

3. ___The hat___ is too little.

4. Sam ___ran down___ the hill.

5. Sam and ___Pam___ can jump.

At Home: Draw a picture to illustrate one sentence on this page.

Name_____

> Every sentence begins with a capital letter.

Write each sentence correctly.

1. this is my cap.

   This is my cap.

2. you can play with me.

   You can play with me.

3. she sat down.

   She sat down.

4. nan ran up.

   Nan ran up.

5. he has the mat.

   He has the mat.

© Macmillan/McGraw-Hill

At Home: Point out the capital letters that begin the sentences on one page of a favorite storybook.

Name_____

> A sentence is a group of words that tells a whole idea.
>
> Every sentence begins with a capital letter.

Write each sentence correctly.

1. we can nap here.

   _____

   We can nap here.

2. she ran and ran.

   _____

   She ran and ran.

3. sam said to go up.

   _____

   Sam said to go up.

4. do not jump.

   _____

   Do not jump.

Add words to make this a sentence.

5. nan has

   _____

   Answers will vary.

© Macmillan/McGraw-Hill

At Home: Write a sentence using the words **man** and **ran**.

Name_____

Fill in the circle next to the complete sentence.

1. ● Pam has to go.

   ○ not up here.

   ○ hat for Sam.

2. ○ Pat and Sam.

   ● We jump down.

   ○ is with you.

3. ● Nan ran to me.

   ○ up and down the mat.

   ○ Tan has.

4. ○ a little pat for the cat.

   ○ ran and ran.

   ● The cats can go up.

5. ○ the mat is.

   ● Sam can play.

   ○ my little cap.

At Home: Review this page together.

Name_____

The words in a sentence have to be in the right order.

The order has to make sense.

Correct: Sam ran over my cap.

Not correct: Ran cap Sam my over.

Circle the sentences that have the words in the right order.

1. (Dan jumps over the hat.)

2. It we over jump.

3. (Pat tags Dan.)

4. (She plays tag, too.)

5. Ran Sam here back.

At Home: Put the words in items 2 and 5 in the right order.

Name_____

The words in a sentence have to be in the right order.
The order has to make sense.

Write the words in order.

1. Looks Mack up.

Mack looks up.

2. My has bag he.

He has my bag.

3. Jump to said Pat.

Pat said to jump.

4. Bag over Mack the jumps.

Mack jumps over the bag.

5. It, we too do.

We do it, too.

At Home: Make up a story about a cat. Use three sentences.

Name_____

> Every sentence ends with a special mark.
>
> Example: The man ran back.

Put the correct mark at the end of each sentence.
Circle the mark.

1. Look at me go so fast _____ (!)

2. Mack ran like this _____ (.)

3. She jumps over it _____ (.)

4. Hal is over there _____ (.)

5. Can we play here _____ (?)

6. Wow, this is what I like to do _____ (!)

At Home: Write sentences about things to do on rainy days. Include end marks.

Name _____

> The words in a sentence must make sense.
>
> A sentence ends with a special mark .

Look at the sentences. Write <u>C</u> if a sentence is correct. Fix the others by writing the words in order.

I. Not Pam can go.

Pam can not go.

2. He has the map.

C

3. The cat sat on it.

C

4. Down jumps she up and.

She jumps up and down.

5. Sam can see Hal.

C

At Home: Draw a picture to illustrate one of the sentences on this page.

Name_____

Put an X next to sentences with the words out of order.

Put the words in order. Write the sentences correctly on the lines.

1. my is cat. Mack   **X**

_____
Two possible answers.
_____
Mack is my cat.   My cat is Mack.

2. over the mat. jump He can   **X**

_____

He can jump over the mat.

3. Sam has a bag for Mack.

_____

_____

4. Mack likes to play with it.

_____

_____

5. too. He Sam, likes   **X**

_____

He likes Sam, too.

At Home: Review this page together.

A statement tells something.
Example: Wag is little.

Draw a line under the statements.

1. Wag naps and naps.
_____

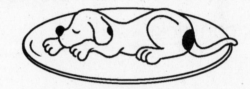

2. Digs too

3. Wag has my cap.
_____

4. He runs to me.
_____

5. Rides

6. Wag and I play.
_____

© Macmillan/McGraw-Hill

At Home: Create statements for the items you did not underline.

How You Grew • Book 1.1/Unit 1   11

Name_____

A statement tells something.

Example: Jan can ride.

Draw a line from the statement to its picture.

1. Jack can kick.

2. Pam runs.

3. The hat is too big.

4. Val has the bat.

At Home: Write sentences about what you do at recess.

© Macmillan/McGraw-Hill

Name_____

A statement begins with a capital letter.
A statement ends with a period.

Write each statement correctly.

1. Jack is quick

   Jack is quick.

2. he rides up and down

   He rides up and down.

3. Pam packs the bag

   Pam packs the bag.

4. she can do it

   She can do it.

5. we are big

   We are big.

At Home: Tell about something you can do by yourself that
you couldn't do when you were a baby.

How You Grew • **Book 1.1/Unit 1**   13

© Macmillan/McGraw-Hill

A statement is a sentence that tells something. A statement begins with a capital letter and ends with a period.

Read each pair of statements.

Circle the statement that is correct.

1. (She runs and jumps.)

   We jump, too

2. he sits down

   (Jack rides with me.)

3. (My cap is in here.)

   Pam can not see it

4. (Sam can play this.)

   You can do it

At Home: Draw a picture of something you would like to do when you get older.

© Macmillan/McGraw-Hill

Name ______________________________

Draw a line under the statements.

1. In the bag
   He packs up.
   Looks

2. This, too
   In here
   She said yes.

3. A big hat
   The hat fits me.
   Sees it

4. We can ride.
   Jumps over
   Val and Rick

5. Will be
   Kicks and runs
   Rick wins.

At Home: Review this page together.

A question is a sentence that asks something.

Example: Where is that cat?

An exclamation is a sentence
that shows strong feeling.

Example: Help, I can't find the cat!

Write <u>Q</u> or <u>E</u> next to each question or exclamation.

1. Is the cat there? _____Q_____

2. Help, the cat is not here! _____E_____

3. Did the cat go up? _____Q_____

4. Did the cat come down? _____Q_____

5. I can not see that cat! _____E_____

6. The cat played a trick! _____E_____

Write a question on the line.

_____

Questions will vary.
_____

At Home: Change the statements to questions.

Name_____

An exclamation is a sentence that shows strong feelings.

Example: What a fat cat that is!

A questions is a sentence that asks something.

Example: Where did the cat go?

Circle the exclamations and underline the questions.

1. (Come here, quick!)

2. What is it?

3. (Look at that!)

4. (What a good cat you are!)

5. Where did the little cat go?

6. (Grab the cat!)

At Home: Find pictures of three animals. If you could ask each one a question, what would you ask?

A question ends with a question mark.

Example: Can Pal do a trick?

An exclamation ends with an exclamation mark.

Example: That was a good trick!

Circle the correct end mark for each sentence.

Write the mark on the line.

1. Look out for Pal _____!_____   ?   (!)

2. Grab him _____!_____   ?   (!)

3. Will he jump on me _____?_____   (?)   !

4. He is too quick _____!_____   ?   (!)

5. What can we do _____?_____   (?)   !

6. Can we trick Pal _____?_____   (?)   !

At Home: Create exclamations about a favorite pet or animal.

© Macmillan/McGraw-Hill

Name _____

> A question asks something.
> A question ends with a question mark.
>
> An exclamation shows strong feelings.
> An exclamation ends with an exclamation mark.

Write each sentence correctly. Write C if a sentence is correct.

1. What is on the mat!

   What is on the mat?

2. That is big!

   C

3. Grab the cat quick?

   Grab the cat quick!

4. Can we come in!

   Can we come in?

5. Is this a trap?

   C

At Home: Talk about an exciting day in your life. Use exclamations.

Pet Tricks • **Book 1.1/Unit 1**   **19**

© Macmillan/McGraw-Hill

Name _____

Put a question mark or an exclamation mark at the end of each sentence.

1. Come here, quick _____**!**_____

2. What is that in the grass _____**?**_____

3. Look at it jump up _____**!**_____

4. Will it jump on me _____**?**_____

5. Grab my hat _____**!**_____

6. Run, run, run _____**!**_____

7. Do you see it _____**?**_____

8. Where did it go _____**?**_____

At Home: Review this page together.

© Macmillan/McGraw-Hill

Name_____

A sentence is a group of words that tells a whole idea. Every sentence begins with a capital letter and ends with a special mark.

**Write each sentence correctly.
Begin with a capital letter.
Add the end mark shown in ( ).**

1. she can use my help (period)

_____

She can use my help.

2. where did it land (question mark)

_____

Where did it land?

3. look at it go up (exclamation mark)

_____

Look at it go up!

4. the wind will help now (period)

_____

The wind will help now.

© Macmillan/McGraw-Hill

At Home: Look through a favorite story. Find examples of sentences that end with a period, a question mark, and an exclamation mark.

Name_____

Every sentence begins with a capital letter. Every sentence ends with a special mark.

Circle the sentence that is correct in each group.

1. hank runs fast

   Hank runs fast

   (Hank runs fast.)

2. can we help him win

   (Can we help him win?)

   can we help him win?

3. (He wins!)

   he wins

   He wins

Write a sentence that tells what can happen next.

_____

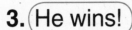 Sentences will vary.

At Home: Write a story about a sports race. Use statements, questions, and exclamations.

Name _____

> Begin every sentence with a capital letter.
> End every sentence with a special mark.

Unscramble the words in the box to complete the sentence. Write the sentence correctly.

1. we | sand can this use
_____

We can use this sand.

2. will | it help do you me
_____

Will you help me do it?

3. look | crab that very little at
_____

Look at that very little crab!

4. where | the go crab did
_____

Where did the crab go?

At Home: Draw a picture to illustrate your answer to item 3.

Name_____

Write C if a sentence is correct. If a sentence is not correct, write the letter or letters to tell how you would make it right.

(A)   Begin with a capital letter.

(B)   Put a special mark at the end.

(C)   Do not change.

1. (r)ick jumps on the mat.   _____ A _____

2. Will Pam run fast**?**   _____ B _____

3. (s)he can go like the wind**! or .**   _____ A, B _____

4. Now Sam runs and jumps.   _____ C _____

5. (d)id he land in the sand?   _____ A _____

6. That was a very good jump!   _____ C _____

Go back to the sentences. Circle any letter that should be capital. Put the correct mark at the end.

At Home: Point out the capital letters at the beginning of sentences in a favorite story.

Read the sentences. Write them correctly.

will you help, too

can you pick up bricks

here are the bricks, Dad

what a big help you are

we like to help you

Write two statements from the box. Order of sentences 1 and 2 may vary.

1. Here are the bricks, Dad

2. We like to help you.

Write two questions from the box.

Order of sentences 3 and 4 may vary.

3. Will you help, too?

4. Can you pick up bricks?

Write one exclamation from the box.

5. What a big help you are!

Name_____

A noun is a word that names a person, a place, or a thing.

Say the name of the noun in the picture.

person   place   thing

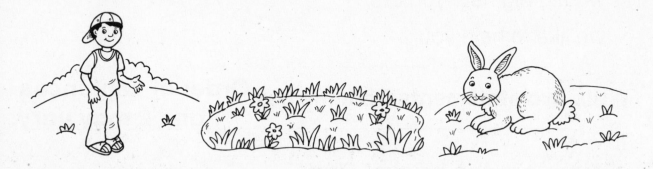

Circle the noun in each sentence.

1. Look at the little (dog.)

2. It sits in the (grass.)

3. The (mom) runs over.

4. They see an (ant.)

5. It digs up (sand.)

6. What a big (hill) that is!

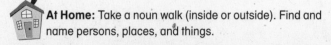

At Home: Take a noun walk (inside or outside). Find and name persons, places, and things.

© Macmillan/McGraw-Hill

Name_____

A noun is a word that names a person, place, or thing.

Write the noun from the word box to complete each sentence. Circle all the nouns in each sentence.

pond   pad   dad   rock   frog

1. The little _____ **frog** _____ jumps on the (log)

2. The (mom) is in the _____ **pond** _____.

3. Is that big fat (frog) the _____ **dad** _____?

4. The (dad) sits on a _____ **rock** _____.

5. They jump on the _____ **pad** _____.

© Macmillan/McGraw-Hill

🏠 **At Home:** Identify the nouns circled on this page. Tell whether the nouns name a person, place, or thing.

Animal Moms and Dads 27
Book 1.2/Unit 2

Name_____

> A sentence begins with a capital letter.
>
> A statement ends with a period.
>
> Example: The cat sat in the hat.

Read each pair of sentences.
Circle the statement that is correct.

1. the mom is with her kit

  (The mom is with her kit.)

2. A kit is a little fox?

  (A kit is a little fox.)

3. (Mom helps the little fox.)

  Mom helps the little fox

4. now they play in the grass.

  (Now they play in the grass.)

At Home: Name five jungle animals and five sea creatures.
Explain why these words are nouns.

© Macmillan/McGraw-Hill

Name_____

A noun names a person, place, or thing.

Most sentences contain nouns.

Begin every sentence with a capital letter.

End every statement with a period.

Write the statement correctly. Circle the nouns.

I. i see one little cat

_____

I see one little (cat).

2. it can not go over the log

_____

It can not go over the (log).

3. a cat does not jump like a frog

_____

A (cat) does not jump like a (frog).

4. the mom will help

_____

The (mom) will help.

© Macmillan/McGraw-Hill

At Home: Look for nouns in a favorite storybook and say them out loud.

Animal Moms and Dads

Book 1.2/Unit 2

29

Look at the underlined words in each sentence. Write the one that is a noun.

1. I <u>am</u> a quick <u>little</u> <u>pig</u>. _____ pig _____

2. Look at me <u>run</u> <u>down</u> the <u>hill</u>. _____ hill _____

3. My <u>mom</u> <u>said</u> <u>to</u> come back. _____ mom _____

4. <u>Help</u> your <u>dad</u> <u>now</u>. _____ dad _____

5. I can <u>bring</u> <u>this</u> big <u>log</u> to him. _____ log _____

6. Can I <u>play</u> <u>with</u> my good <u>pal</u> now? _____ pal _____

At Home: Review this page together.

© Macmillan/McGraw-Hill

Name_____

A plural noun names more than one person, place, or thing.
Add **-s** to make most nouns plural.

Example: one **cat**   two **cats**

Circle the plural noun in each sentence.

1. Mom has a lot of (jobs) to do.

2. The (kids) like to help her.

3. Pam will fix the (beds).

4. The (dogs) have to eat now.

5. Jack does the (pots) in the sink.

6. Now we can have some (eggs).

© Macmillan/McGraw-Hill

At Home: Illustrate the plural nouns circled in each sentence.

Little Red Hen • **Book 1.2/Unit 2**   **31**

Name_____

A plural noun names more than one person, place, or thing.

Add **-es** to form the plural of nouns that end with **s**, **ss**, **sh**, **ch**, or **x**

Example: one **kiss**   two **kisses**

Write a plural noun to complete the sentence. The picture and words in the box will help.

branch	glass	box	dish

1. Will you help pack the

   _____
   _ _ _ _ _ _ _ _ _
   boxes ?
   _____

2. This one is for pots and

   _____
   _ _ _ _ _ _ _ _ _
   dishes .
   _____

3. That box is for mom's best

   _____
   _ _ _ _ _ _ _ _ _
   glasses .
   _____

   _____
   _ _ _ _ _ _ _ _ _
4. What is on the ___ **branches** ___?

At Home: Reread a favorite story to find plural nouns that end in **-s** or **-es**.

Name_____

A sentence begins with a capital letter.
A question ends with a question mark.

Write the questions correctly.

1. who will help me get the eggs

_____

Who will help me get the eggs?

2. will the hens peck at me

_____

Will the hens peck at me?

3. can we go to see the pigs now

_____

Can we go to see the pigs now?

4. what do the little pigs eat

_____

What do the little pigs eat?

© Macmillan/McGraw-Hill

At Home: Discuss chores that have to be done at home.
Write questions about helping out with these chores at home.

Little Red Hen • **Book 1.2/Unit 2** 33

Name_____

Add **-s** or **-es** to form the plural of most nouns. Begin every sentence with a capital letter. End a question with a question mark.

Find the mistakes. Circle the letters that should be capital. Underline the nouns that should be plural. Add the correct end mark.

1. (w)ill you help me up**?**

2. (w)ho fell on all the egg**?**

3. (t)he two cat jumped on me.

4. (w)here are they now**?**

5. (d)o you see some little leg over there**?**

6. (w)hat is in the two bush**?**

At Home: Write each sentence correctly on a piece of paper. Talk about the corrections that were made.

© Macmillan/McGraw-Hill

Name _____

Write the plural for each noun.

1. pet _____ pets _____

2. box _____ boxes _____

3. egg _____ eggs _____

4. dish _____ dishes _____

5. glass _____ glasses _____

6. lunch _____ lunches _____

Write two sentences about how you help at home. Use one or two of the plural nouns you wrote in each sentence.

7. _____ Sentences will vary. Each sentence should _____

8. _____ contain at least one of the plural nouns from _____ items 1–6.

At Home: Review this page together.

Name_____

Some plural nouns do not end with **-s** or **-es**. These nouns use a new word to name more than one.

Say the nouns and their plurals.

child   children   man   men

goose   geese   mouse   mice

foot   feet

Circle the plural or plurals in each group.

1. mouse   man   (geese)

2. (men)   foot   child

3. goose   (children)   (feet)

4. man   child   (mice)

At Home: Choose four plural nouns from above. Write a sentence for each noun.

Name

Some plural nouns use a new word to name more than one.

Choose the plural noun that belongs in each sentence. Write it on the line.

1. The (men, mans) fish at the pond. ___**men**___

2. The (children, childs) play with a little ship. ___**children**___

3. They see the prints of many (feet, foots) in the sand.

___**feet**___

4. Do (mouses, mice) live here? ___**mice**___

5. No. The (gooses, geese) live in the pond. ___**geese**___

At Home: Make up silly sentences using the irregular plural nouns written on the lines above.

Name_____

> A sentence begins with a capital letter.
>
> An exclamation ends with an exclamation mark.

Find the exclamation in each pair.

Put a check [✓] next to the exclamation.

Circle the exclamation mark.

1. Look at the mice!) ✓
   Where do they live?

2. They live in the man's shop.
   The mice will eat his socks!) ✓

3. Don't eat my socks!) ✓
   What will the man do?

4. He will bring two cats into the shop.
   Run, mice, run!) ✓

At Home: Tell a story based on one or more of the irregular plurals found above.

© Macmillan/McGraw-Hill

Name_____

Remember that some nouns use new words to name more than one. Begin every sentence with a capital letter. End an exclamation with an exclamation mark.

Write C if a sentence is correct.
If a sentence is not correct, circle the mistakes.

1. Don't go in the pond! C

2. (the) (gooses) will not like it.

3. (that) goose is very mad now(?)

4. (Childs), get out quick(.)

5. She can peck with her bill! C

At Home: Identify the mistakes in the sentences and discuss how to fix them.

A Prairie Dog Home • **Book 1.2/Unit 2** 39

Name_____

Circle the correct plural for each noun.

1. goose

   gooses   (geese)   geeses

2. foot

   (feet)   footes   foots

3. man

   (men)   mans   mens

4. child

   childs   childrens   (children)

Write the plural for the word in ( ) to complete the sentence.

5. The ____**mice**____ hid in the grass. (mouse)

At Home: Review this page together.

Name_____

A noun that names a special person or place is called a proper noun. A proper noun begins with a capital letter.

Examples: **Y**an   **J**ill   **T**exas

Write the proper noun in each group.

1. Rick   drum   play   _____**Rick**_____

2. humm   Hal   he   _____**Hal**_____

3. Lin   kids   fun   _____**Lin**_____

4. show   let's   Jen   _____**Jen**_____

5. Atlanta   shop   she   _____**Atlanta**_____

At Home: Make up a sentence using all three words in numbers 1, 3, and 6.

Name_____

A proper noun names a special person or a special place. Some proper nouns are more than one word. Each word in a proper noun begins with a capital letter.

Miss **P**ink   **W**est **S**treet

Buck **H**ill **S**chool

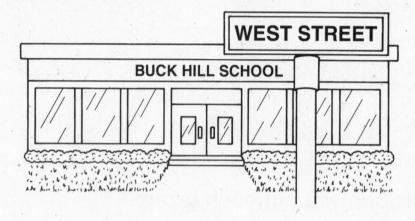

Underline the proper nouns in each sentence.

I. Where is the <u>Land School</u>?

2. It's on <u>Frank Street</u>.

3. Go past <u>Red Duck Pond</u> to get to it.

4. <u>Miss Winn</u> wants to put on a show.

5. <u>Pam</u> will be in the show, too.

6. She used to live in <u>Putnam, Vermont</u>.

At Home: Write and illustrate sentences using family names as proper nouns.

© Macmillan/McGraw-Hill

A proper noun names a special person or special place. A proper noun begins with a capital letter.

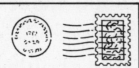

Hank Little
123 Jump Street
Dallas, Texas 75201

Follow the directions to write proper nouns.

1. Write your first and last name.   **Answers will vary.**

2. Write your address.

(street)

(city, state, zip code)

3. Write the name of your school.

4. Write your teacher's name.

At Home: Make a sign for a mailbox that includes names of family members, street address, and town or city.

The Fun Kids' Band • **Book 1.2/Unit 2**   43

© Macmillan/McGraw-Hill

Begin a proper noun with a capital letter. Some proper nouns are more than one word. Begin each word in a proper noun with a capital letter.

Circle the words that should have capital letters.

1. Al and (pam) go to the (banks school).

2. (miss ann) has a good band there.

3. "I play the drums," said (chan)

4. I got them in a shop on Tip (top street).

5. The band will play in (new york) City.

6. Will (nick) sing with the band?

At Home: Rewrite the words that have been circled. Be sure to use capital letters.

Name_____

Rewrite the sentences. Begin each proper noun with a capital letter.

1. Here comes the band from crest school.

_____

Here comes the band from Crest School.

2. They come down frost street.

_____

They come down Frost Street.

3. My pals rick and tan play in the band.

_____

My pals Rick and Tan play in the band.

4. miss hill and the kids sing.

_____

Miss Hill and the kids sing.

5. They sing three texas songs.

_____

They sing three Texas songs.

© Macmillan/McGraw-Hill

Name _____

> Some proper nouns name the days of the week. Some proper nouns name the months. The name of the days and the months begin with capital letters.

Say the days. Circle the capital letters.

Monday   Tuesday   Wednesday

Thursday   Friday   Saturday   Sunday

Say the months. Circle the capital letters.

January   February   March   April

May   June   July   August

September   October   November   December

I. What day do you like best?

_____

_ _ _ _ _ _ _ _ _ _ _ _ _ _ _ _ _

_____

2. What month do you like best?

_____

_ _ _ _ _ _ _ _ _ _ _ _ _ _ _ _ _

_____

Answers will vary.

At Home: Ask questions such as "What day comes before Tuesday?" and "What month comes between March and May?"

Name_____

Days, months, and holidays are proper nouns.
All proper nouns begin with capital letters.

Write the word that completes the sentence correctly.

1. Today is _____**Thursday**_____. (Thursday, thursday)

2. I do not go to school in _____**June**_____. (june, June)

3. We put the flag out for _____**July 4**_____.
   (july 4, July 4)

4. We will have lots of fun on _____**Saturday**_____.
   (Saturday, saturday)

5. Some kids start school in _____**August**_____.
   (august, August)

At Home: Talk about favorite holidays. Choose one special
day and write a sentence about why this day is special.

Name_____

Some proper nouns name holidays.
Holiday names begin with capital letters.

Examples: Thanksgiving   Valentine's Day

Draw a line to match the holiday to its picture.

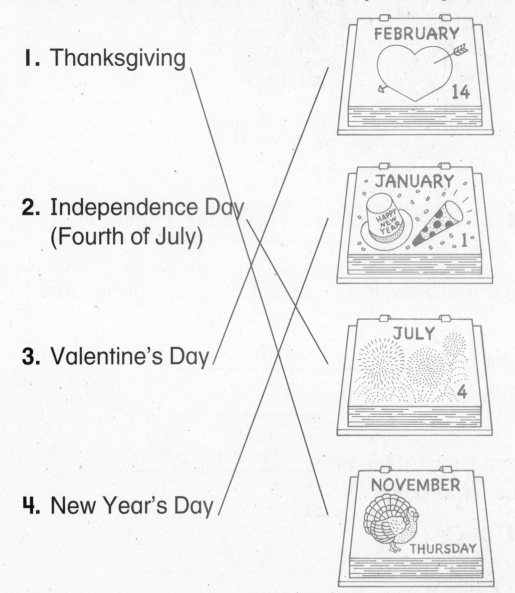

1. Thanksgiving

2. Independence Day
(Fourth of July)

3. Valentine's Day

4. New Year's Day

© Macmillan/McGraw-Hill

 At Home: Create a collage of the days and months by writing
the names and cutting them from magazines and newspapers.

Name_____

> Begin the names of days, months, and holidays with capital letters.

Circle the letters that should be capital. Write the day, the month, or the holiday correctly.

1. We had fun on (n)ew (y)ear's (d)ay. ___**New Year's Day**___

2. That was in (j)anuary. ___**January**___

3. Today is (t)uesday, February 14. ___**Tuesday**___

4. Then it must be (v)alentine's Day ___**Valentine's Day**___

5. On (m)onday, we put little red flags at school.

___**Monday**___

6. What fun things can we do in (m)arch?

___**March**___

At Home: Create and illustrate a family Special Days calendar for this month.

On My Way to School **49**
Book 1.2/Unit 2

© Macmillan/McGraw-Hill

Name_____

Underline the name of the day, month or holiday in each sentence. Write C if the name is written correctly. Write NC if the name is not correct. Then write it correctly.

1. We have no school on <u>thursday</u>.

   _____

   NC, Thursday

2. It is <u>Thanksgiving</u>.

   _____

   C

3. School is out on <u>friday</u>, too.

   _____

   NC, Friday

4. Are you going away in <u>december</u>?

   _____

   NC, December

5. We will be back on <u>new year's day</u>.

   _____

   NC, New Year's Day

6. It will be <u>January</u> then.

   _____

   C

At Home: Review this page together.

© Macmillan/McGraw-Hill

Name

A verb is a word that shows action.

Examples: Jake **jumps**.   Fran **runs**.

verb

**Find the verb in each group. Fill in the circle.
The first one is done for you.**

1. ○ today
   ● jump
   ○ for

2. ● ride
   ○ we
   ○ three

3. ○ man
   ● make
   ○ it

4. ○ who
   ○ some
   ● eat

5. ○ not
   ● play
   ○ on

6. ● go
   ○ of
   ○ many

7. ● pull
   ○ very
   ○ good

8. ○ now
   ● help
   ○ me

© Macmillan/McGraw-Hill

At Home: Make up and write sentences using the verbs on this page.

Kate's Game • Book 1.3/Unit 3   **51**

Name_____

A verb is a word that shows action.

Write a verb from the box to complete the sentence. The pictures can help.

| pull | jumps | play | wins | run |

1. My pals and I _____**play**_____ games.

2. We _____**run**_____ to the gate.

3. Tran _____**jumps**_____ over the blocks.

4. One, two, three, _____**pull**_____!

5. Jane _____**wins**_____ the big race.

At Home: Think of actions that happened today. Act out some of these actions.

Name_____

A comma (,) comes after the greeting and the closing in a letter.

Dear Jan, (greeting)

I miss you. Do you like where you live now?

Your pal, (closing)
Val

1. Circle the commas after the greeting and closing in this letter.

Dear Fred,

Can you come to see me Monday?

Your pal,
Rick

2. Put commas after the greeting and closing in this letter.

Hello Liz,

I won a big race. It was fun!

Your pal,
Ann

At Home: Rewrite the greeting and closing in sentence 2.
Replace the names with family names.

Kate's Game • **Book 1.3/Unit 3** 53

Name_____

Use verbs to show action.

Put commas after the greeting and the closing in a letter.

This letter is missing two commas and three verbs. Add the verbs from the box. Add the commas.

saved	baked	ate

Hello Nan,

_____

Mom and I _____**baked**_____ a cake. Then

we _____**ate**_____ some. It was very good. I

_____**saved**_____ some for you in a tin. Come to

see me. Then you can have some cake, too.

Your best pal,

Pam

At Home: Write a short letter to a friend or close family member.

Name_____

Circle the verb in each sentence.

1. We (went) to Gram's.

2. My pal Mack (fed) my cat.

3. He (walked) my dog, too.

4. We (came) back on the plane.

5. The plane (landed) at 6 P.M.

6. I (thanked) Mack.

Write two sentences about how you help your friends. Circle the verbs.

_____

7. Sentences will vary. Verbs should be circled.

_____

_____

8. _____

© Macmillan/McGraw-Hill

At Home: Review this page together.

Name_____

The tense of a verb tells when an action happens.
Present-tense verbs tell about action that
happens now.

Examples: Dell **makes** a cake.   Pam **helps**.

Circle the verbs in the present tense.
Write them on the lines below.

1. Bob (trips) on the rug.

2. He (drops) his box.

3. The blocks spilled out.

4. Ann rushed over.

5. She (puts) them back in the box.

_____   _____   _____
    trips   drops   puts

At Home: Use the present-tense words circled above to write a new sentence for each verb.

© Macmillan/McGraw-Hill

Name _____

> Present-tense verbs tell about action that happens now.
>
> Add **-s** to most verbs to form the present tense.
>
> jump + s = jumps

Write a present-tense verb to complete each sentence. Add -s to the verb in ( ).

1. Dad ___takes___ care of the plants. (take)

2. His son ___wants___ to help. (want)

3. He ___gets___ the big tin can. (get)

4. He ___fills___ it with water. (fill)

5. Then he ___brings___ it over to Dad. (bring)

© Macmillan/McGraw-Hill

At Home: Create two more sentences in the present tense to describe other ways the son helps.

Name _____

The important words in a book title begin with a capital letter.

The first word of a book title is always capitalized.

The title of a book is underlined.

Examples: <u>The Girl in the Red Hat</u>

Underline the book title that is correct.

1. Kids help out

   <u>Kids Help Out</u>

2. <u>People Who Care</u>

   people who care

3. <u>How Can I Help?</u>

   How can I help?

4. Let's get together

   <u>Let's Get Together</u>

At Home: Look at favorite storybooks and copy the titles on paper.

Name_____

Write C if a sentence is correct. If a sentence is not correct, write the letter or letters to tell how you would make it right.

Ⓐ   Add **-s** to make present-tense verb.

Ⓑ   Capitalize a letter.

1. He looks at the book.   _____ C _____

2. She pick up the dishes.   _____ A _____

3. He dig up the land for Mom.   _____ A _____

4. the boy take care of the hens.   _____ A, B _____

5. He gets the eggs.   _____ C _____

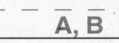

At Home: Think of a present-tense verb for a favorite activity. Write and illustrate a sentence using that verb.

Kids Can Help • **Book 1.3/Unit 3** 59

Make these sentences tell about the present.
Underline the correct verb in ( ).

1. Chan (help, helped, <u>helps</u>) Mom today.

2. He (get, <u>gets</u>, got) a pan for her.

3. Mom (use, used, <u>uses</u>) two eggs.

4. She (<u>adds</u>, added, add) a cup of water.

5. Dad (ate, <u>eats</u>, eat) with them.

6. Mom (look, looked, <u>looks</u>) at the clock.

7. Chan (<u>walks</u>, walked, walk) to the bus.

8. He (wave, <u>waves</u>, waved) to Mom and Dad.

At Home: Review this page together.

Name_____

> A past-tense verb tells about action that happened in the past.
>
> Examples: The boys **washed** up.
>
> Then they **jumped** into bed.

Put a check next to the sentence that tells about the past. Circle the past-tense verb.

1. Sam (played) with shadows. ✓

   Sam plays with shadows.

2. Chuck watches him

   Chuck (watched) him. ✓

3. Sam shows Chuck a dog shape.

   Sam (showed) Chuck a dog shape. ✓

4. Chuck (liked) that one best. ✓

   Chuck likes that one best.

At Home: Make up sentences about things that happened yesterday. Act out several of these sentences.

Short Shadows, Long Shadows
Book 1.3/Unit 3   **61**

Name _____

Past-tense verbs tell about actions that already happened.

Most verbs in the past tense end in **-ed**.

watch   +   ed   =   watched

Use a verb from the box to complete the sentence. Circle the -ed ending in the verb.

| walked | blinked | wanted | pulled | looked |

1. I _____ blinked _____ at the sun in my face.

2. Mom _____ pulled _____ down the shade.

3. The cat _____ walked _____ into the den.

4. We _____ looked _____ at its shape on the shade.

5. Then the cat _____ wanted _____ to eat.

© Macmillan/McGraw-Hill

At Home: Find and circle examples of past-tense words in a newspaper.

Name _____

> A proper noun begins with a capital letter.
>
> Examples: **Mitch** lived in **Texas**.

Write the sentences. Capitalize the proper nouns.

1. pam went on a whale watch.

   _____

   Pam went on a whale watch.

2. She and mom got to the dock late.

   _____

   She and Mom got to the dock late.

3. The dock is on fish lane.

   _____

   The dock is on Fish Lane.

4. Did nick see the ship in the water?

   _____

   Did Nick see the ship in the water?

5. One ship came from the city of paris.

   _____

   One ship came from Paris.

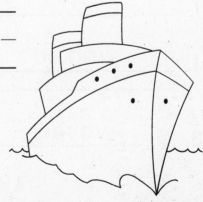

© Macmillan/McGraw-Hill

At Home: Name and write a proper noun for **girl, boy, street, school.**

Name _____

Read the story. Circle the letters that should be capital letters. Underline four verbs that should be past tense. Write the verbs in the past tense on the lines below.

Dad and (j)ames went for a walk. They <u>walk</u> past (f)itch (l)ane. Miss (C)hin <u>yell</u> hello to them. They <u>wave</u> to her. The sun was going down. James <u>look</u> back. "I can see my shadow!" he said.

The order of answers may vary.

1. _____walked_____

2. _____yelled_____

3. _____waved_____

4. _____looked_____

At Home: Continue the story to tell what happened next. Use past tense verbs in the sentences.

© Macmillan/McGraw-Hill

Name_____

Circle all the past tense verbs.

1. (pitched)   looks   cares   (walked)

2. pats   make   (made)   (went)

3. (sat)   (lived)   (ran)   jumps

4. (liked)   pulls   (said)   drinks

5. drag   (sang)   (used)   (helped)

Rewrite each sentence to tell about the past. Change the underlined verb to past tense.

6. We <u>watch</u> the sun come up.

_____

We watched the sun come up.

7. The kids <u>play</u> in the shade.

_____

The kids played in the shade.

8. Ann and Seth <u>want</u> a drink.

_____

Ann and Seth wanted a drink.

Name_____

The verbs **is** and **are** tell about the present.

Is tells about one person, place, or thing.

Are tells about more than one person, place, or thing.

Examples: Dad **is** there.

The cats **are** here.

Circle the verb in each sentence. Write <u>1</u> if the verb tells about one. Write <u>2</u> if the verb tells about more than one.

1. Mom (is) out back. _____1_____

2. Our two dogs (are) with her. ___2___

3. The twins (are) in the water. ___2___

4. Mom (is) on chair. _____1_____

5. This game (is) so much fun! _____1_____

Name_____

> Use the verb **is** to tell about one person, place, or thing.
>
> Use the verb **are** to tell about more than one person, place, or thing.

Write <u>is</u> or <u>are</u> to complete each sentence.

1. My things _____ are _____ all over the place.

2. Kim _____ is _____ here to help.

3. The blocks _____ are _____ in the box.

4. My space _____ is _____ not a mess now.

At Home: Find the one or more than one person, place, or thing that the verb tells about in each of the sentences.

Smile Mike! • **Book 1.3/Unit 3** 67

© Macmillan/McGraw-Hill

Name_____

> Every sentence begins with a capital letter. A statement ends with a period. An exclamation ends with an exclamation point.

Write the statements correctly.

1. we are all here

_____

We are all here.

2. gram is with us, too

_____

Gram is with us, too.

3. our bags are in the tent

_____

Our bags are in the tent.

Write the exclamations correctly.

4. look out for that black stick

_____

Look out for that black stick!

5. that is a snake, not a stick

_____

That is a snake, not a stick!

At Home: Write four sentences about a family vacation or class field trip. Use two statements and two exclamations.

Name _____

Find the mistakes. Cross out the verb if it is wrong. Write the correct verb above it. Circle any letters that should be capital. Add the correct end mark if one is missing. (Hint: Each sentence has two mistakes.)

1. The little kids ~~is~~ *are* in the den ___ . ___

2. (d)on't let the dogs in here . *or* !

3. (h)ide the game, quick ___ !

4. (i)t ~~are~~ *is* too late.

5. (t)he dogs ~~is~~ *are* on our game!

6. This ~~are~~ *is* not that funny . *or* !

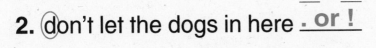

At Home: Write two sentences that use the verb **is**. Write two sentences that use the verb **are**.

Smile Mike! • **Book 1.3/Unit 3** 69

© Macmillan/McGraw-Hill

Name_____

Write is or are to complete each sentence.

1. "It _____ is _____ time," Mom said.

2. Jane and I _____ are _____ in our best dresses.

3. Giles and Nick _____ are _____ in back of us.

4. Giles _____ is _____ so funny.

5. Our smiles _____ are _____ very, very big!

Write a sentence about your family. Use is or are in the sentence.

6. Sentences will vary, but should contain the verb is or are.

At Home: Review this page together.

© Macmillan/McGraw-Hill

Name _____

A contraction is a short way of saying and writing two words.

Two words: **are not   does not**

                           ↓   ↓

Contractions: **aren't   doesn't**

Draw a box around the contractions you find.

1. We can't go skating now.

2. Gram wasn't on the bus.

3. I didn't see her.

4. Why hasn't Gram called?

5. Isn't that Gram?

6. I couldn't find my skates.

At Home: Create sentences about things to do with family members. Use a contraction on this page in each sentence.

Name_____

A contraction is a short form of two words. The two words are put together and letters are left out. An apostrophe (') shows where letters have been left out.

Example: She **isn't** here. (is not = isn't)

Look at all the snow!

Look at the underlined contraction. Circle the two words used to make the contraction.

1. Papa <u>wasn't</u> at his shop. Papa (was not) at his shop.

2. We <u>didn't</u> go to school. We (did not) go to school.

3. They <u>aren't</u> walking the dogs.

   They (are not) walking the dogs.

4. Gram <u>couldn't</u> ride her bike.

   Gram (could not) ride her bike.

5. The buses <u>weren't</u> running.

   The buses (were not) running.

At Home: Find contractions in favorite storybooks.

Name_____

A contraction is a short form of two words. An apostrophe (') takes the place of letters that are left out to make the contraction.

Write the contraction for the underlined words in each sentence.

I. Splash <u>does not</u> want to help.   _____ doesn't

2. "That <u>is not</u> fun," he said.   _____ isn't

3. He <u>would not</u> scrub the pans.   _____ wouldn't

4. He <u>did not</u> scrape the dishes.   _____ didn't

5. "You <u>are not</u> going to play," Mom said. _____ aren't

© Macmillan/McGraw-Hill

At Home: Create a story about Splash and his family. Use as many contractions as possible.

Name_____

A contraction is a short way of writing and saying two words.

Use an apostrophe (') to take the place of letters that are left out of a contraction.

Circle the contractions that are not correct.
Write the contractions correctly.
Write C if the contraction is correct.

1. Mom (doesnt') like us to be late.　　**doesn't**

2. You (arent) going to miss the bus!　　**aren't**

3. The bus (isnt) here yet.　　**isn't**

4. It wasn't on time.　　**C**

5. We are glad it (did'nt) splash us.　　**didn't**

Use the words in ( ) to form a contraction. Write the contraction to complete the sentence.

1. Gram _____**isn't**_____ in here. (is not)

2. She _____**wasn't**_____ out back. (was not)

3. I _____**didn't**_____ see her on the deck. (did not)

4. Gram _____**wouldn't**_____ hide in there. (would not)

5. Why _____**don't**_____ we call her? (do not)

6. We _____**haven't**_____ looked in all her hiding places yet. (have not)

© Macmillan/McGraw-Hill

Name_____

The verbs **was** and **were** tell about the past.

Was tells about one person, place, or thing.

Were tells about more than one person, place, or thing.

Examples: Little Red **was** in the nest.

Mom and Dad **were** there, too.

Circle the verb that belongs in the sentence.

1. The sun (was, were) up.

2. Three eggs (was, were) in the nest.

3. One egg (was, were) not in the nest.

4. Dad (was, were) away from the nest.

5. Mom and Little Red (was, were) on a branch.

At Home: Draw an arrow from the verb to the person(s), place(s), or thing(s) that the verb describes.

Name_____

Use the verbs **was** and **were** to tell about the past.
Use **was** to tell about one person, place, or thing.
Use **were** to tell about more than one person, place, or thing.

Write <u>was</u> or <u>were</u> to complete the sentence.

1. Our school play _____was_____ today.

2. All the kids _____were_____ in it.

3. Kim and Joe _____were_____ little bugs.

4. I _____was_____ a rose bush.

5. One boy _____was_____ a robin.

6. The funny hats _____were_____ for Kim and Ted.

At Home: Make up and illustrate sentences about natural settings. Use **was** and **were** in each sentence.

Name_____

A proper noun names a special person, place, or thing. A proper noun begins with a capital letter.

Read each row of words. Circle the word or words that should begin with capital letters.

1. girl   (fran)   (bob)

2. (mike)   he   (elm lane)

3. hill   (grove school)   home

4. boy   soon   (miss rose)

Fill in the blanks to complete the sentences. Use the proper nouns you circled above.

5. _____**Fran**_____ and _____**Mike**_____ were

on _____**Elm Lane**_____. They were walking to the

_____**Grove School**_____.

6. Wasn't that _____**Miss Rose**_____ at the bus stop?

Order of people's names may vary.

At Home: Write a sentence using two proper nouns that were circled but not used in items five and six.

© Macmillan/McGraw-Hill

Use **was** to tell about one.

Use **were** to tell about more than one.

Capitalize proper nouns.

Find four mistakes in the story. Circle the mistakes. Write the sentences correctly on the lines.

Hal lives on plum lane. Jon came to play. The two boys was out back. They saw a robin in a nest. Lots of bugs were in the grass. One bug were not good. It wanted to bite hal on the nose.

1. Hal lives on Plum Lane.

2. The two boys were out back.

3. One bug was not good.

4. It wanted to bite Hal on the nose.

© Macmillan/McGraw-Hill

At Home: Reread the story. Then write a new ending for the story.

Pelican Was Hungry
Book 1.4/Unit 4
79

Name_____

Circle and write <u>was</u> or <u>were</u> to complete each sentence.

1. Six white gulls _____ **were** _____ on the sand.

   was   (were)

2. One gull _____ **was** _____ on the post.

   (was)   were

3. Some fish _____ **were** _____ under the water.

   was   (were)

4. Soon, all the gulls _____ **were** _____ together.

   was   (were)

5. The gull's bill _____ **was** _____ opened wide.

   (was)   were

6. That _____ **was** _____ a big splash!

   (was)   were

At Home: Review this page together.

© Macmillan/McGraw-Hill

Name_____

> The verbs **has** and **have** tell about the present.
>
> **Has** tells about one person, place, or thing.
>
> **Have** tells about more than one person, place, or thing.
>
> Examples: Lulu **has** an old glass.
>
> Pru and Zack **have** some cans.

Underline the verb if it tells about one.
Circle the verb if it tells about more than one.

1. The kids (have) work to do.

2. Pru <u>has</u> a black bag for the cans.

3. Zack <u>has</u> lots of cans.

4. Lulu and Dad (have) glass things.

5. Mom <u>has</u> a box for glass.

6. The two girls (have) big piles of stuff.

© Macmillan/McGraw-Hill

At Home: Make up sentences about keeping a neighborhood clean. Use **have** or **has** as the verb in each sentence.

June Robot Cleans Up
Book 1.4/Unit 4

81

Name_____

> The verb **has** tells about one person, place, or thing.
>
> The verb **have** tells about more than one person, place, or thing.

Put parts together to write a sentence. The first one is done for you. Circle the verbs.

My pal Chan   have fun together.

Your bag   has a big hole in it.

Ann and Bill   have string on them.

The two piles   has a box of games.

1. My pal Chan (has) a box of games.

2. Your bag (has) a big hole in it.

3. Ann and Bill (have) fun together.

4. The two piles (have) string on them.

At Home: Name the verb in each sentence above and say if it tells about one or more than one.

Name _____

Every sentence begins with a capital letter.

A statement ends with a period.

A question ends with a question mark.

Write each sentence correctly.

1. what does Joe have in the sack

_____

What does Joe have in the sack?

2. joe has some pine cones for us

_____

Joe has some pine cones for us.

3. do you have string to hang the cones

_____

Do you have string to hang the cones?

4. the flock has a nice place to eat now

_____

The flock has a nice place to eat now.

 At Home: Brainstorm events from today. Write a statement and a question about these happenings.

© Macmillan/McGraw-Hill

Name_____

Find the mistakes. Write the letter or letters that tell how you would fix the mistake.

A Change the verb to **has** or **have**.

B Begin with a capital letter.

C Add an end mark.

D Do not change.

(1) Some people do not care about our land

(2) do you see all the junk on the sand?

(3) Now, Carlos and Rosa has to pick it up.

(4) doesn't the sand look good now

(5) Carlos and Rosa have cans and glass to take home.

(6) Mom have a good use for them.

_____   _____

1. _____C_____   2. _____B_____

3. _____A_____   4. ___B, C___

5. _____D_____   6. _____A_____

At Home: Write the sentences with mistakes correctly on another piece of paper.

Write <u>has</u> or <u>have</u> to complete each sentence.

1. These all _____**have**_____ a blank side.

2. He _____**has**_____ a used brush.

3. We _____**have**_____ some brushes.

4. Tekla _____**has**_____ a good plan.

5. The girls and boys _____**have**_____ fun.

6. This one _____**has**_____ a funny face on it.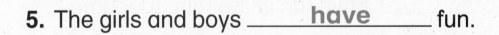

Name_____

> The verbs **go** and **do** have different forms to tell about the present and the past.
>
> | Present | Past |
> |---|---|
> | He **goes**. We **go**. | We all **went**. |
> | She **does**. They **do**. | We all **did**. |

Write the verb that tells about the present.

1. Jay _____**goes**_____ outside to play. (goes, went)

2. Al _____**does**_____ not like to splash. (does, did)

3. We _____**do**_____ have fun in the rain. (do, go)

Write the verb that tells about the past.

4. When _____**did**_____ the sun come out? (do, did)

5. May and Lulu _____**went**_____ for a walk. (go, went)

6. I _____**went**_____ in when it got cold. (goes, went)

At Home: Draw a picture and write a sentence about a rainy day activity. Use a form of **go** or **do** in the sentence.

Name_____

The verbs **go** and **do** have different forms for the present tense and the past tense.

Present: **go, goes**   **do, does**

Past: **went**   **did**

**Underline the present tense forms of <u>go</u> or <u>do</u>.
Circle the past tense forms of <u>go</u> or <u>do</u>.**

1. The rain <u>goes</u> plop, plop, plop!

2. (Did) you hear that great big clap?

3. Why <u>does</u> it have to rain so much?

4. The lights (went) out.

5. What will we <u>do</u> now?

Write a sentence about the weather. Use the past tense of <u>go</u> or <u>do</u>.

6. _____

   Sentences will vary. Sentences should
   _____

   contain the verb went or did.

At Home: Change the tense of the verbs on this page from present to past, or from past to present.

Name_____

Begin proper nouns with capital letters. If the name of a person or place is more than one word, capitalize all the important words.

Sam Shade   Flop the Fish

Circle the letters that should be capital. Write the proper nouns correctly.

1. ⓣank the ⓣiger went outside with his son.
   _____

   Tank, Tiger

2. "See how the sun goes in and out," ⓢtripe said.
   _____

   Stripe

3. I do not like the sound of the wind," said ⓟapa ⓐpe.
   _____

   Papa Ape

4. "The air does have a chill," said ⓢnap the Snake.
   _____

   Snap

5. "Did anyone watch the news?" Mama ⓐpe said.
   _____

   Ape

At Home: Make name cards for your family. Put first, middle, and last names on one side. Put nicknames on the other.

© Macmillan/McGraw-Hill

Name_____

The verbs **go** and **do** use different forms to tell about the present and the past. The names of people and places begin with capital letters.

Read the story. Circle four sentences with mistakes. Write the sentences correctly.

One day, West Wind goed wild. "I will make it very cold," west wind said. That will be fun." That do not sound like fun to Sunray. So sunray shined and shined. Soon it got very warm. "Now that's fun!" she said.

1. One day, West Wind went wild.

2. "I will make it very cold," West Wind said.

3. That did not sound like fun to Sunray.

4. So Sunray shined and shined.

At Home: Think up names based on weather words for other characters. Draw the characters and label them.

Stormy Weather • Book 1.4/Unit 4 **89**

© Macmillan/McGraw-Hill

Name_____

Underline a form of the verb <u>go</u> or <u>do</u> in each sentence. Write Present or Past to tell the tense of the underlined verb.

1. My cat <u>does</u> not like the rain. _____present_____

2. She <u>goes</u> under the chair to hide. _____present_____

3. My dogs <u>do</u> like the rain. _____present_____

4. They <u>went</u> out when Mom came in. _____past_____

5. <u>Did</u> they get all wet? _____past_____

6. Mom makes them <u>go</u> to the shed. _____present_____

© Macmillan/McGraw-Hill

Name_____

The verb **see** has a special form to tell about the past.

Present	**Past**
She **sees**. We **see**.	He **saw**. They **saw**.

Circle the verb that tells about the present.

1. Jean (looked, (sees), saw) the leaf.

2. We look close to (does, (see), was).

3. Pat (ran, (sees), saw) many lines on the leaf.

Circle the verb that tells about the past.

4. Sue (see, (saw), sees) a little bug.

5. Pat and Sue (see, sees, (saw)) a bug.

6. They (go, do, (saw)) a big bug.

 At Home: At the end of each day this week, answer these:
What did you see today? What did you say today?

The verb **see** has a different form for the present tense and the past tense.

Present: **see, sees**

Past: **saw**

Circle sentences that tell about the present. Underline sentences that tell about the past.

1. We saw a play about Ben Franklin.

2. Ben cannot see well.

3. "I will make new glasses so people can see."

4. Ben's son Will sees a kite and string.

5. Will saw that it was raining outside.

6. Ben saw a bolt of lightning.

7. Ben says, "I'll show you."

At Home: Read the sentences to a family member. Point out **see** or **saw** and tell whether it is present or past.

© Macmillan/McGraw-Hill

Use commas in a letter
- after the greeting and the closing,
- between the day and year in a date,
- between the name of a city and state.

Circle the commas in this letter.

June 30, 1752

Dear Peter,

My idea worked. I said it would. Come see me in Philadelphia, Pennsylvania.

Your friend,

Ben

Add the missing commas in this letter.

May 10, 1815

Dear Granddad,

Do you like living in Bath, Maine? Mom said we can visit soon. I'll bring my new kite.

Your best girl,

Lena

© Macmillan/McGraw-Hill

At Home: Look through old letters or postcards from friends and relatives. Draw a circle around all the commas.

Read the letter.

Two commas are missing. Three verbs are wrong.

Add the missing commas. Cross out the verbs that are wrong.

Write the verbs in the correct tense on the lines below.

September 3, 1922

Dear Nana,

    Yesterday Dad ~~see~~ a little house in our elm tree. "It's a bat house," he said.

    Then, my friends came over. We saw five bats go in the house. We ~~sees~~ the bats hanging upside down.

    Bats are fun to ~~sees~~.

      Your grandson,

      Joe

saw

saw

see

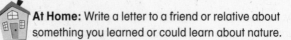

At Home: Write a letter to a friend or relative about something you learned or could learn about nature.

Name_____

Write the correct tense of <u>see</u> to complete each sentence.

1. Al and Jo can _____ **see** _____ Mom fill a pot with water.

2. They _____ **saw** _____ her do the same thing last Sunday.

3. Mom now _____ **sees** _____ Al and Jo.

4. "I _____ **saw** _____ you eat that!" says Mom.

Write two sentences. Use the past tense of <u>see</u>.

Sentences will vary but should use saw.

7. _____

8. _____

Name_____

A contraction is a short way of saying and writing two words.

Many contractions are formed with **not**. An **apostrophe** (') takes the place of the letters that are left out.

Examples: do + not ⟶ don't

does + not ⟶ doesn't

Match the underlined words to contractions. Write the sentence letter on the line. The first one is done for you.

A. "This <u>is not</u> funny," said Bunny.

B. "You <u>are not</u> good friends."

C. "I <u>did not</u> do it," said Frog.

D. "I <u>was not</u> the one," said Skunk.

E. "We <u>were not</u> here," they said.

F. "We <u>could not</u> have opened the box."

1. isn't _____A_____   2. wasn't _____D_____

3. weren't _____E_____   4. didn't _____C_____

5. couldn't _____F_____   6. aren't _____B_____

At Home: Read the sentences aloud with the contractions in place of the underlined words.

Name _____

A **contraction** is a short form of two words. An **apostrophe** (') takes the place of the letters that are left out.

Write a contraction from the word box for the underlined words.

don't   haven't   wasn't   wouldn't   couldn't

1. Little Spot <u>would not</u> help clean up. _____ **wouldn't** _____

2. Mama Spot <u>was not</u> very happy. _____ **wasn't** _____

3. Little Spot <u>could not</u> go out to play. _____ **couldn't** _____

4. "I <u>do not</u> like sad endings," Beth said. _____ **don't** _____

5. "I <u>have not</u> come to the end,"
   _____ **haven't** _____
   said Dad.

© Macmillan/McGraw-Hill

At Home: Make up a new ending for Little Spot's story. Draw a picture and write a sentence using a contraction.

Little Rabbit and the Falling Fruit
Book 1.4/Unit 4   **97**

Name_____

> An **apostrophe** (') takes the place of the **o** in **contractions** formed with **not**.
>
> Example: have + not = haven't

Write a contraction for the two words in ( ).

1. "I _____ **don't** _____ think Bumpy is home," Sandy said. (do not)

2. "He _____ **isn't** _____ in here taking a bath," said Big Green Frog. (is not)

3. "He _____ **didn't** _____ jump in the pond for a swim," said White Swan. (did not)

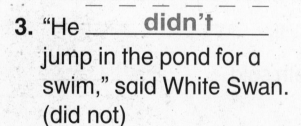

4. Bumpy _____ **wasn't** _____ anywhere Sandy looked. (was not)

At Home: Look for contractions formed with **not** in a favorite book.

© Macmillan/McGraw-Hill

Name_____

A **contraction** is a short form of two words. Use an **apostrophe** (') to take the place of the **o** in contractions formed with **not**.

Make a check mark [✓] next to the sentence with the correct contraction. Circle the contraction.

I. The fox (couldn't) get the grapes. ✓

The fox couldnt get the grapes.

2. The boy (wasn't) telling a joke. ✓

The boy wasnt' telling a joke.

3. The rabbit did'nt win the race.

The rabbit (didn't) win the race ✓

4. The man doe'snt keep the yelling fish.

The man (doesn't) keep the yelling fish. ✓

5. The cat and mice (aren't) friends. ✓

The cat and mice arent friends.

THE FOX AND THE GRAPES AND OTHER TALES

At Home: Tell what words form the contractions on this page.

Little Rabbit and the Falling Fruit
Book 1.4/Unit 4 99

© Macmillan/McGraw-Hill

Mark the contraction for the underlined words.

1. "This <u>does</u> <u>not</u> look good," said Bunny.

   ○ didn't   ○ don't   ● doesn't

2. "That <u>was</u> <u>not</u> a great idea," Fox said.

   ● wasn't   ○ wouldn't   ○ weren't

3. "I <u>did</u> <u>not</u> want you to do it," Bear said.

   ○ don't   ○ isn't   ● didn't

4. "Mom <u>is</u> <u>not</u> going to like it," said Bunny.

   ○ won't   ● isn't   ○ wasn't

5. "I <u>do</u> <u>not</u> like it!" Mama Rabbit said.

   ○ won't   ● don't   ○ doesn't

6. "You <u>have</u> <u>not</u> got any hair!"

   ○ can't   ○ hasn't   ● haven't

© Macmillan/McGraw-Hill

 At Home: Review this page together.

Name_____

An **adjective** is a word that tells about a noun.
A **noun** is a person, place, or thing.

That is a **great** painting.

      /   \

   adjective   noun

Circle the adjective in each sentence. Underline the noun it tells about. The first one is done for you.

1. The boat is sailing on a (deep) <u>sea</u>.

2. A (little) <u>girl</u> stands on the deck.

3. The (cold) <u>wind</u> blows her hair.

4. The (big) <u>sails</u> flap in the wind.

5. People wave from a (sandy) <u>beach</u>.

6. They had a (terrific) <u>day</u>.

At Home: Point to objects in the room and say an adjective to describe each object.

Olivia • **Book1.5/Unit 5** (101)

© Macmillan/McGraw-Hill

An **adjective** is a word that tells about a noun. Some adjectives tell what kind. Some adjectives tell how many.

Examples: <u>**What kind**</u>   <u>**How many**</u>

a **nice** boy   **three** girls

the **silly** dog   **many** cats

Circle the adjectives that tell what kind. Underline the adjectives that tell how many.

1. Those are (cute) pigs.

2. I used (new) clay to shape them.

3. Who made the <u>six</u> ducks?

4. What (funny) tails those pigs have!

5. This hen has <u>some</u> chicks.

6. This (little) chick fell down.

At Home: Think of new adjectives that tell what kind or how many for the nouns on this page.

Name _____

> The name of a special person or place is a **proper noun.** Proper nouns begin with capital letters.

Circle the proper noun in each sentence.
Write it correctly on the line.

1. (val) has some sand in glasses and bags. _____ Val _____

2. Is the sand from (jones beach)? _____ Jones Beach _____

3. No, (mother) got it at a little shop. _____ Mother _____

4. The shop is on (main street.) _____ Main Street _____

5. Now (amy) puts in red sand. _____ Amy _____

At Home: Look in a magazine or newspaper for proper nouns. Point to the capital letters.

Olivia • Book 1.5/Unit 5   103

© Macmillan/McGraw-Hill

Name_____

Read the letter. Circle six words that should begin with capital letters.

Dear (mike,)

Would you like to come to the (shoat) Gallery with us? It is on (elm) (street) in the city. (dad) says we will see some great paintings there. We are going in two weeks.

Your friend,
Sandy (wan)

Write the sentence correctly. Add an adjective to tell more about the underlined nouns.

1. The name of the <u>girl</u> who painted that <u>daisy</u> is joan reed.

_____

Adjectives will vary. The name Joan Reed

_____

should be capitalized.

At Home: Write a sentence that tells about a favorite place you and a special friend or family member like to go.

Name_____

Write an adjective to tell about the underlined noun.

1. Who made that _____pretty_____ quilt?

2. It has _____nine_____ squares.

3. Look at the _____cute_____ sheep.

4. A _____loud_____ sound scared them.

5. The sheep ran down the _____steep_____ hill.

6. Now the _____little_____ girl can't find them.

Answers will vary. Accept all reasonable answers. Possible answers are given.

© Macmillan/McGraw-Hill

Name_____

Add **-er** to an adjective to compare two people, places, or things.

Example: Jon is **faster** than Mike.

Add **-est** to an adjective to compare three or more people, places, or things.

Example: Ed is the **fastest** boy on the team.

Write the adjectives that compare.

	add -er	add -est
1. low	lower	lowest
2. sweet	sweeter	sweetest
3. kind	kinder	kindest

Underline the adjectives that compare.

4. My dog is <u>slower</u> than Tim's dog.

5. It is <u>bigger</u> than Pedro's train.

6. It is the <u>cutest</u> dog in the bunch.

At Home: Take turns making up sentences with the adjectives that compare on this page.

© Macmillan/McGraw-Hill

Name_____

Add **-er** to an adjective to compare two people, places, or things.

Add **-est** to an adjective to compare three or more people, places, or things.

Write the adjective that completes the sentence correctly.

1. Al's kite has the ___**longest**___ tail of all the friends.

   longer   longest

2. This is the ___**highest**___ spot in the whole park.

   highest   higher

3. The wind is ___**colder**___ now than before.

   coldest   colder

4. Kim's kite is ___**newer**___ than Rob's kite.

   newer   newest

5. Mine is the ___**biggest**___ kite of all in the sky.

   bigger   biggest

At Home: Read aloud the sentences with the adjectives in place. Tell what is being compared in each sentence.

Name_____

Every sentence begins with a capital letter.
Every sentence ends with a special mark.

Circle the sentence that is correct.

1. which plane has longer wings?

   (Which plane has longer wings?)

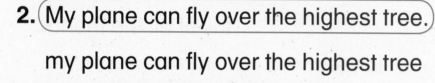

2. (My plane can fly over the highest tree.)

   my plane can fly over the highest tree

3. (His plane is lighter than yours.)

   his plane is lighter than yours?

4. Is that the fastest plane of all

   (Is that the fastest plane of all?)

5. Push the littlest plane out of the way

   (Push the littlest plane out of the way!)

At Home: Write a sentence about a favorite toy. Make sure the sentence begins with a capital letter and has an end mark.

© Macmillan/McGraw-Hill

Name_____

**Look for mistakes with adjectives that compare.
Look for mistakes with capital letters and end marks.**

**Write X if a sentence
has any mistakes.**

**Write C if a sentence
is correct.**

1. what makes the sticks fly up _____ X _____

2. You have to spin them in the air. _____ C _____

3. Which of the three sticks will spin for the long time

   of all? _____ X _____

4. Ruby's stick makes a soft sound than mine does. _____ X _____

5. Catch the stick before it drops! _____ C _____

6. my stick has a wider top than Jen's _____ X _____

© Macmillan/McGraw-Hill

At Home: Explain how you would fix the sentences you
marked with **X**.

Circle the adjective that compares in each sentence.
Write 2 if the adjective compares two.
Write 3 if the adjective compares three or more.

1. Lee has the (newest) bike of all.   _**3**_

2. Pam's bike is (lighter) than Rosa's.   _**2**_

3. This bus is (bigger) than that bus.   _**2**_

4. The (oldest) boat at the dock broke down.   _**3**_

5. The (smallest) plane landed late.   _**3**_

6. Which of those two trains is (longer)?   _**2**_

7. The (fastest) sled dog leads the pack.   _**3**_

8. My dog is (slower) than a mule.   _**2**_

At Home: Review this page together.

Name_____

An adjective tells about a noun. Some adjectives tell the color of something.

Examples: **blue** sky

Find the color word in each sentence.
Write it on the line.

1. Look at the yellow roses. _____ yellow

2. The black cat ran away. _____ black

3. Wait until the green light comes on. _____ green

4. The baby girl has a pink nose. _____ pink

5. Do you like my red coat? _____ red

© Macmillan/McGraw-Hill

At Home: Play "I spy," using color words. One person says "I spy something red." The other guesses what's red.

Name _____

Some adjectives tell what color something is.

Circle the color word in each sentence.

1. What can your new (gray) robot do?

2. It made me this (tan) scarf.

3. It can drive our big (blue) machine.

4. It can fix my old (green) cart.

5. My barn was (white).

6. It painted my barn (red).

At Home: Find a colorful picture in a storybook. Write two sentences about the picture, using color words.

© Macmillan/McGraw-Hill

Name _____

> Contractions that are formed with the word **not** use an apostrophe (') to take the place of the letter **o.**

Write the sentences. Replace the underlined words with a contraction.

1. The yellow bus <u>was not</u> on time.

_____

The yellow bus wasn't on time.

2. We <u>could not</u> get into the white tent.

_____

We couldn't get into the white tent.

3. The boys on the blue bikes <u>are not</u> staying.

_____

The boys on the blue bikes aren't staying.

4. They <u>do not</u> need their green tickets.

_____

They don't need their green tickets.

5. We <u>did not</u> see any red smoke.

_____

We didn't see any red smoke.

© Macmillan/McGraw-Hill

At Home: Read aloud the sentences you wrote with the contractions. Point out the color words in the sentences.

Kids' Great Inventions
Book 1.5/Unit 5

113

Name_____

Read the story. Cross out (X) four contractions that are wrong. Write C above two contractions that are correct.

The old black cat wa~~x~~'nt happy. He
di~~d~~nt like having mice in his house.
"I am going to catch those mice," he
said.

    C
"We don't want that to happen,"
the little gray mice said. But the cat
was little. The mice cou~~l~~dnt tell when
he was coming. So they made an
alarm.

When the cat stepped on a red rug
in the hallway, a green bell rang.
    C
The mice hid. "The cat can't catch
us," they said. "Now we ar~~e~~nt going
to leave."

At Home: Reread the story aloud. Explain how to fix the
contractions that are wrong. Draw a picture for the story.

© Macmillan/McGraw-Hill

Name _____

Circle the color word in ( ) to complete the sentence.

1. Mr. Whiz put on a (white, hat, long) coat.

2. He got into his (see, like, blue) machine.

3. The (square, hard, green) screen lit up.

4. One of the (pink, low, two) lights blinked.

5. He pulled the (little, yellow, go) switch.

6. (Dry, Gray, What) smoke filled the air.

7. There was a (red, loud, box) flash.

8. He was flying in (out, black, low) space.

© Macmillan/McGraw-Hill

Name_____

Some adjectives are words for numbers.

one	two	three	four	five
1	2	3	4	5
six	seven	eight	nine	ten
6	7	8	9	10

Circle the number word in each sentence. Draw a line to the picture it tells about.

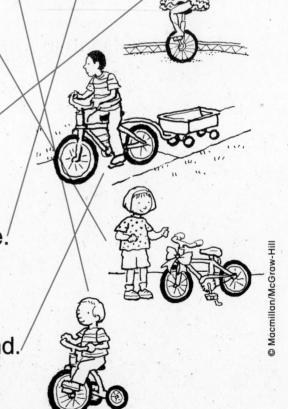

1. The baby's bike has (three) wheels.

2. Pam's new bike has (two) wheels.

3. She rides a bike with (one) wheel.

4. There are (four) wheels on that bike.

5. See (six) wheels go round and round.

© Macmillan/McGraw-Hill

At Home: Say a number rhyme, like "One two, buckle my shoe." Write the number words you hear in the rhyme.

Name _____

> Some adjectives are words for numbers.
>
> Example: There are **seven** children on the track.

Complete the sentence. Write the number word that stands for the number in ( ).

1. The track is ____ one ____ mile long. (1)

2. There are ____ eight ____ kids on my team. (8)

3. I couldn't run fast when I was ____ four ____. (4)

4. Now I am ____ seven ____ and run very fast. (7)

5. I beat ____ five ____ runners in a race. (5)

6. My team has won ____ ten ____ races. (10)

At Home: Write two of the sentences on this page again.
Use a different number word in each sentence.

Name_____

> The days of the week are proper nouns. The names of the days begin with capital letters.

Write the word that is correct.

1. Mark can do just one spin on

_____ **Thursday** _____.

thurs.   Thursday   thursday

2. He tried to do three spins on ____ **Tuesday** ____.

Tuesday   tues   tuesday

3. He fell down six times on ____ **Wednesday** ____.

wed.   wednesday   Wednesday

4. By ____ **Friday** ____, he can spin four times.

fri.   friday   Friday

5. He spins five times on

_____ **Sunday** _____.

sun.   Sunday   sunday

At Home: Make a calendar for the week. Write in things you have do each day.

© Macmillan/McGraw-Hill

Name

Circle the mistakes in these sentences.

Then write the sentences correctly.

Write number words for numbers in each sentence.

Begin the names of days with capital letters.

1. I was 7 last (saturday.)

_____

I was seven last Saturday.

2. On (sunday,) the 4 of us see a show.

_____

On Sunday, the four of us see a show.

3. The man keeps 6 pins in the air.

_____

The man keeps six pins in the air.

4. I try hard on (monday) and (tuesday.)

_____

I try hard on Monday and Tuesday.

At Home: Talk about something your family does to celebrate one of the summer holidays.

**Circle the number words in the box.
Then write number words from the box to
complete the sentences.
Use a word only once.**

(two)	big	puppy	(four)	(seven)
red	(nine)	(five)	clean	(ten)
(three)	(eight)	(one)	(six)	new

1. I can keep _____ balls in the air.

2. Lin can lift _____ bags of blocks.

3. Joey can go up _____ stairs at a time.

4. Rosa can run and jump _____ feet.

1–4. Answers will vary. Children should use
number words from the box, and should not use
the same number word more than once.

© Macmillan/McGraw-Hill

At Home: Review this page together.

Name_____

> Words that have the same or almost the same meaning are called **synonyms.**
>
> **Synonyms:** smile   grin
>
>   shine   glow
>
> Words that have opposite meanings are called **antonyms.**
>
> **Antonyms:** new   old
>
>   up   down

Read each row of words.

Circle the two words that are synonyms.

1. (kind)   happen   (nice)   ground

2. (small)   plant   big   (little)

3. (happy)   (glad)   mean   grow

Circle the two words that are antonyms.

4. dig   (before)   (after)   from

5. (all)   seeds   (none)   great

6. (wet)   care   again   (dry)

At Home: Think of 3 pairs of synonyms and 3 pairs of antonyms that are not on this page.

A Fruit Is a Suitcase for Seeds   121
Book 1.5/Unit 5

© Macmillan/McGraw-Hill

Name _____

Find the word in the second sentence that means the same as the underlined word in the first sentence. Write both words on the lines.

I. When will you <u>start</u> the homework?

I will begin it now.

_____

start, begin

2. I was <u>sick</u> on Tuesday.

My friend was ill, too.

_____

sick, ill

Find the word that means the opposite of the underlined word. Write both words.

3. We got an <u>early</u> start.

We worked until it was late.

_____

early, late

4. Look at how <u>big</u> the plant has grown.

It came from such a little seed.

_____

big, little

 At Home: Look for synonyms and antonyms as you read a favorite story.

© Macmillan/McGraw-Hill

Name_____

The important words in a book title begin with capital letters. Book titles are underlined.

Look at the books. Then write the book titles correctly to answer the questions.

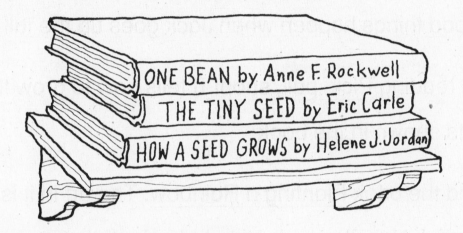

ONE BEAN by Anne F. Rockwell

THE TINY SEED by Eric Carle

HOW A SEED GROWS by Helene J. Jordan

1. What book is by Eric Carle?

_____

The Tiny Seed

2. What book by Helene Jordan tells how a seed grows?

_____

How a Seed Grows

3. What book is about growing a bean plant?

_____

One Bean

© Macmillan/McGraw-Hill

At Home: Write the titles of two of your favorite books.
Check to see that the titles are capitalized correctly.

A Fruit Is a Suitcase for Seeds
Book 1.5/Unit 5
123

Name_____

Read about books. Find the book title. Write <u>C</u> above the title if it is written correctly. Write <u>NC</u> if it is not correct.

NC
1. The book <u>jack and the beanstalk</u> is about Jack and a

   tiny seed that grows into a big plant. Jack is a good boy.

   But bad things happen when Jack goes up the tall plant.

NC
2. I am reading <u>Pick, pull, snap!</u> It tells how to grow the

   plants shown in the book.

C
3. I liked the book <u>Planting a Rainbow</u>. The art in it is

   beautiful. Now I know how to help plants grow.

Write the wrong titles correctly on the lines.

Jack and the Beanstalk

Pick, Pull, Snap!

At Home: Find one pair of synonyms and two pairs of antonyms in item 1.

© Macmillan/McGraw-Hill

Name

Read the story.

Write S if the underlined words in each part are synonyms.

Write A if the underlined words are antonyms.

The little plant wanted to be as big as the other plants

in the garden. _____ A _____

He tried to stretch his stem, but he couldn't reach up

any higher. _____ S _____

"I don't like being short," he said. "I want to be tall

now." _____ A _____

"Wait," his sister said. "It takes some time. The sun will shine on you. Rain will fall. Water will drop onto the dirt. You will soak in the water. Then you will grow."

_____ S _____

"Is there a faster way? " he said.

"There's no quicker way," she said.

_____ S _____

A sentence is made up of two parts.

The **subject** of a sentence is the part that tells **who** or **what** the sentence is about.

Example: An ant is on the leaf.

What is on the leaf?

An ant is. **An ant** is the subject.

Answer the question to find the subject of each sentence. Write the subject.

1. Flies have wings.

_____

What has wings? _____ Flies _____

2. That tiny spider made a big web.

_____

What made a big web? _That tiny spider_

3. Mr. Jones takes care of bees.

_____

Who takes care of bees? ____ Mr. Jones ____

4. Bees buzz near the hive.

_____

What buzzes near the hive? _____ Bees _____

126 Dot and Jabber and the Big Bug
Mystery • **Book 1.5/Unit 6**

At Home: Use the subjects written above to write a new
sentence for each subject.

© Macmillan/McGraw-Hill

Name_____

> The **subject** of a sentence tells **who** or **what** the sentence is about.
>
> Example: **Pam** knows about bugs.

Make each sentence tell about the picture. Choose a subject from the box. Write the subject on the line.

A grasshopper	Two moths	Six little ants
A butterfly	Many bees	

1. _Many bees_ live in the hive.

2. _Six little ants_ march up the hill.

3. _A butterfly_ lands on the rose.

4. _Two moths_ fly near the light.

5. _A grasshopper_ jumps in the grass.

© Macmillan/McGraw-Hill

At Home: Write three sentences about bugs. Circle the subjects.

Dot and Jabber and the Big Bug Mystery • Book 1.5/Unit 6   **127**

Name_____

A sentence begins with a capital letter and ends with a special mark.

Write each sentence correctly.

1. where is my friend Fuzzy

_____

Where is my friend Fuzzy?

2. little Ant does not know

_____

Little Ant does not know.

3. the other bugs can't find her

_____

The other bugs can't find her.

4. is Fuzzy hiding in that silky case

_____

Is Fuzzy hiding in that silky case?

5. fuzzy is a now a beautiful butterfly

_____

Fuzzy is now a beautiful butterfly.

At Home: Check other sentences you have written. Make sure they begin with capital letters and have end marks.

© Macmillan/McGraw-Hill

Name_____

Read the story. Then write the letter or letters below to show how to fix each sentence in the story.

Ⓐ Add a subject. Ⓒ Add an end mark.

Ⓑ Begin with a capital letter. Ⓓ Do not change.

(1) ant and White Bird didn't get along. (2) One day, Ant fell into the water (3) so White Bird dropped a leaf into the water (4) Got on the leaf. (5) The wind pushed the leaf to the sand. (6) Ant was saved. (7) What happened to Ant and White Bird (8) Have become good friends.

1. ___B___   2. ___C___   3. ___B, C___

4. ___A___   5. ___D___   6. ___D___

7. ___C___   8. ___A___

At Home: Copy the story correctly. Draw your own picture to go with it.

Dot and Jabber and the Big Bug Mystery • Book 1.5/Unit 6   129

© Macmillan/McGraw-Hill

Name_____

Circle the subject in each sentence.

1. (Some bugs) live in the ground.

2. (That dirt pile) is an ant hill.

3. (Ants) live inside.

4. (Henry) likes to watch ants.

5. (This store) sells ant farms.

6. (Mom) thinks ants should live outside.

Write a subject to complete each sentence.

Answers to 7 and 8 will vary.

7. ____A tiny bug____ is on the leaf.

8. ____My friend Joe____ likes all kinds of bugs.

Name

A sentence is made up of two parts: a subject and a predicate.

The **predicate** of a sentence is the action part of the sentence. The **predicate** tells what the subject does or is.

Example: The moon **rises in the night sky**.
The moon **is full**.

Circle the predicate in each sentence.

1. The sun (sets.)

2. The sky (gets dark.)

3. We (see many stars.)

4. The moon (shines down.)

5. A cloud (passes over the moon.)

6. The moon and stars (light the sky.)

© Macmillan/McGraw-Hill

At Home: Point out the predicate in each sentence. Then point out the subject in each sentence.

Little Bear Goes to the Moon

131

Book 1.5/Unit 6

Name_____

The **predicate** is the part of the sentence that tells what the subject does or is.

Example: The ship **went to the moon**.

Write Yes or No to tell if the predicate is underlined in each sentence.

1. The trip <u>took three days</u>. _____Yes_____

2. <u>The ship</u> landed on the moon. _____No_____

3. Two men <u>got out of their ship</u>. _____Yes_____

4. The men <u>walked on the moon</u>. _____Yes_____

5. They picked up <u>moon rocks</u>. _____No_____

6. Their ship <u>blasted off for earth</u>. _____Yes_____

Write the predicates for the sentences you marked No.

<u>Children should write the predicates for items 2</u>

<u>and 5: landed on the moon; picked up moon rocks.</u>

© Macmillan/McGraw-Hill

 At Home: Write a sentence about traveling to the moon. Circle the predicate. Underline the subject.

Name_____

The name of a holiday begins with a capital letter.

**Complete each sentence with a holiday name.
Write the holiday correctly.
Use each holiday name only once.**

mother's day   father's day   thanksgiving
valentine's day   new year's day

**Order of some answers may vary.
Accept reasonable answers.**

1. I gave Dad a book about space for __Father's Day__.

2. We made dinner for Mom on __Mother's Day__.

3. __Thanksgiving__ is a day for us to give thanks.

4. When is __New Year's Day__?

5. This __Valentine's Day__
card is for you.

At Home: Write a sentence about your favorite holiday. Check
to see that the holiday name begins with a capital letter.

Little Bear Goes to the Moon
Book 1.5/Unit 6

133

© Macmillan/McGraw-Hill

Name_____

> A sentence has a subject and a predicate.
>
> Capitalize the name of a holiday.

Write:

- **S** if a sentence is missing a subject.
- **P** if the sentence is missing a predicate.

Circle letters that should be capital in the name of a holiday.

1. Jack gave Dad a great gift for father's Day.

   _____

   _ _ _ _ _ _ _ _ _ _ _

   _ _ _ _ _ _ _ _ _ _ _

2. The gift. _____ P _____

   _ _ _ _ _ _ _ _ _ _ _

3. The two of them. _____ P _____

   _____

   _ _ _ _ _ _ _ _ _ _ _

4. Went to Mars on a rocket ship. _____ S _____

   _____

   _ _ _ _ _ _ _ _ _ _ _

5. They won't be back until thanksgiving. _____

 At Home: Add a subject or a predicate to the sentences that are missing a part. Write the new sentences.

Name _____

Fill in the circle next to the predicate of each sentence.

1. Kim and her dad watch from the ground.
   - ○ Kim and her dad
   - ○ from the ground
   - ◉ watch from the ground

2. Kim's mom is on that space ship.
   - ○ Kim's mom is
   - ◉ is on that space ship
   - ○ on that space ship

3. They take off for a trip in space.
   - ○ They
   - ○ for a trip
   - ◉ take off for a trip in space

4. Their ship goes near the earth.
   - ◉ goes near the earth
   - ○ Their ship goes
   - ○ near the earth

5. Earth looks beautiful from space.
   - ○ Earth
   - ◉ looks beautiful from space
   - ○ Earth looks beautiful

At Home: Review this page together.

A **pronoun** is a word that can take the place of a noun.

Use the pronouns **he, she,** or **it** to take the place of one person or thing.

Pete is a cook. **He** is a good cook.

Use the pronoun **they** to take the place of more than one person or thing.

The girls sing. **They** sing very well.

Circle the pronoun that takes the place of the underlined part of the sentence.

1. Mom and Dad work. (They) work hard.

2. Mr. Wall fixes cars. (He) fixes old cars.

3. Anna sells hats. (She) sells bags, too.

4. The two girls walk dogs. (They) walk all kinds of dogs.

5. My sister makes dresses. (She) makes doll dresses.

At Home: Point out the pronouns **he, she, it,** and **they** in a story. Find the noun or nouns the pronouns replace.

Name _____

A **pronoun** is a word that can take the place of a noun.

Write the sentence. Use a pronoun from the box in place of the underlined subject.

He	She	It	They

1. <u>Mrs. Hook</u> makes clay dolls.

   She makes clay dolls.

2. <u>My sister and friend</u> make them, too.

   They make them, too.

3. <u>The red clay</u> gets very hard.

   It gets very hard.

4. <u>The colorful clay dolls</u> are for sale.

   They are for sale.

5. <u>Dad</u> gets a doll for Mom.

   He gets a doll for Mom.

At Home: Write two sentences about what your family members do at work. Replace their names with pronouns.

© Macmillan/McGraw-Hill

Name_____

> Use a comma
> - between the day and year in a date.
> - between the name of a city and state.
> - after the greeting and closing in a letter.

Put commas where they belong.

1. Mom left her old job on May 16,2004.

2. She got a new job in Dayton,Ohio.

3. June 19,2004

Dear Granddad,

    Mom loves her job. She is very happy. Mr. Walker is her new boss. He said Mom is the best worker in the whole place.

        Your grandson,

        Marco

At Home: Find the pronouns in the letter. Tell what nouns they take the place of.

© Macmillan/McGraw-Hill

Correct the letter. Cross out the underlined words. Write a pronoun to take their place in the space above. Add missing commas.

March 14,1874

Dear Will,

Our new house is done. ~~Our new house~~ **It** is made of

logs. Dad used tree trunks to make the logs. ~~Dad~~ **He** had to

cut down lots of trees.

My sister Kate has her own room now. ~~My sister Kate~~ **She**

is very happy about that.

Next week, Mom and Dad will open their shop in

Dows,Iowa. ~~Mom and Dad~~ **They** will sell food, cloth, and other

goods.

Your best friend,

Hans

 At Home: Choose three pronouns from above. Write a silly sentence for each pronoun.

Cool Jobs • Book 1.5/Unit 6 139

**Rewrite the sentence.
Write a pronoun for the
underlined subject.**

1. My dad has a friend named Willie.

   _____

   He has a friend named Willie.

2. Willie has a fun job.

   _____

   He has a fun job.

3. His job is to make children laugh.

   _____

   It is to make children laugh.

4. Penny works with Willie.

   _____

   She works with Willie.

5. Penny and Willie are clowns.

   _____

   They are clowns.

6. Clowns fall down a lot.

   _____

   They fall down a lot.

© Macmillan/McGraw-Hill

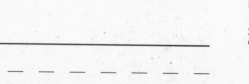
At Home: Review this page together.

Name_____

The words **I** and **me** are pronouns.

Use **I** in the subject of a sentence.

Use **me** in the predicate of a sentence.

Examples: **I** have a book about Baby Bird.
                  Mom gave **me** the book.

Write <u>I</u> in the subject.

1. _____ I _____ am Baby Bird.

2. My sisters and _____ I _____ just hatched.

3. _____ I _____ want some food.

Write <u>me</u> in the predicate.

4. Mom feeds worms to _____ me _____ .

5. She keeps _____ me _____ warm in the nest.

6. Soon, Dad will show _____ me _____ how to fly.

At Home: Imagine you are Baby Bird. Make up more
sentences with **I** or **me** that Baby Bird might say.

Use the pronoun **I** in the subject of a sentence.

Use the pronoun **me** in the predicate of a sentence.

Choose the pronoun that belongs in the sentence. Write it on the line.

1. _____ I _____ want to learn about deer. (I, me)

2. Mom helps _____ me _____ learn. (I, me)

3. She reads _____ me _____ facts about deer. (I, me)

4. _____ I _____ learn that a baby deer is called a fawn. (I, me)

5. Mom shows _____ me _____ a fawn's spots. (I, me)

6. _____ I _____ learn that some deer grow antlers. (I, me)

At Home: Use **I** or **me** in two sentences that explain what you want to learn about an animal that interests you.

© Macmillan/McGraw-Hill

Name_____

The pronoun **I** is always a capital letter.

Example: **I** have a new puppy.

Complete each sentence with I.

1. _____**I**_____ got a puppy
from my Mom and Dad.

2. _____**I**_____ named my puppy Flop.

3. Dad and _____**I**_____ teach Flop to fetch.

4. Every day, _____**I**_____ watch Flop grow bigger and
bigger.

5. _____**I**_____ think Flop
is too big for his bed.

6. Mom and _____**I**_____
give Flop a new bed.

At Home: Find a picture of you as a baby and as you are
now. Make up sentences with **I** to describe the pictures.

Use **I** in the subject of a sentence.

Use **me** in the predicate of a sentence.

Always capitalize the pronoun **I**.

Find mistakes in the play. Circle the pronoun I if it is not written correctly. Make an X on I or me if it is not used correctly.

1. CUBBY: Mama catches fish for I̶.

   Sometimes, (i)eat berries, too.

   I am getting taller and stronger.

2. NUBBY: M̶e want to learn to fish, Mama.

   Cubby and (i)are growing up.

3. MAMA: (i)will teach you to fish, sons.

   You will watch me and learn.

At Home: Read the play aloud for family members. Be sure to use **I** and **me** correctly in the sentences.

© Macmillan/McGraw-Hill

Name_____

Circle the pronoun that belongs in the sentence.
Write it on the line.

1. _____ *I* _____ went to see our new baby horse.

   Me   He   (I)

2. Dad tells _____ *me* _____ it is called a colt.

   she   (me)   I

3. Dad and _____ *I* _____ watch the colt try to stand.

   it   (I)   me

4. _____ *I* _____ will watch the colt grow up.

   (I)   Me   It

5. The colt does not know _____ *me* _____ yet.

   she   I   (me)

6. One day, the colt will be friends with _____ *me* _____.

   it   I   (me)

© Macmillan/McGraw-Hill

Grammar

Name_____

Combining Sentences

Sentences with the same subject or predicate can be put together using the word **and**. Maria can <u>make a fort</u>. Ed can <u>make a fort</u>.

Maria and Ed can make a fort.

**Circle parts that are the same.
Use <u>and</u> to join the sentences.
Write the new sentence.**

1. (Mom) hammers. (Mom) saws.

_____

Mom hammers and saws.

2. Maria (will haul wood). Ed (will haul wood).

_____

Maria and Ed will haul wood

3. (Maria) sands. (Maria) paints.

_____

Maria sands and paints.

4. (Ed gets a) mop. (Ed gets a) broom.

_____

Ed gets a mop and a broom.

5. Nana (will help). Papa (will help).

_____

Nana and Papa will help.

© Macmillan/McGraw-Hill

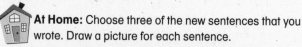

At Home: Choose three of the new sentences that you wrote. Draw a picture for each sentence.

Name _____

> Two sentences can have the same subject or predicate.
> Use **and** to combine the two sentences into one.

**Underline the parts that can be joined by <u>and</u>.
Write the new sentence.**

1. Penny Pig gets <u>bricks</u>.

Penny Pig gets <u>mud</u>.

_____

Penny Pig gets bricks and mud.

2. She will be <u>warm</u>.

She will be <u>dry</u>.

_____

She will be warm and dry.

3. <u>Suzi Pig</u> will not help.

<u>Pauly Pig</u> will not help.

_____

Suzi Pig and Pauly Pig will not help.

4. Now those lazy pigs are <u>wet</u>.

Now those lazy pigs are <u>cold</u>.

_____

Now those lazy pigs are wet and cold.

🏠 **At Home:** Make up sentences to tell what you think happens
to the three pigs next. Use **and** to join subjects or predicates.

Name_____

The pronoun **I** is always a capital letter.

A proper noun begins with a capital letter.

Write the sentence correctly.

1. Paco and i play in my tree house.

_____

Paco and I play in my tree house.

2. i live close to new york city.

_____

I live close to New York City.

3. My best friend is paco Ortez .

_____

My best friend is Paco Ortez.

4. He and i both go to oak hill school.

_____

He and I both go to Oak Hill School.

5. mr. ortez teaches and coaches there.

_____

Mr. Ortez teaches and coaches there.

At Home: Rewrite one or more of the sentences on this page to tell about yourself.

Name_____

> Use **and** to make two sentences into one.
>
> Always capitalize the pronoun **I**.
>
> Always capitalize proper nouns.

Circle letters that should be capital letters. Underline the parts of the sentences that should be joined. Write the new sentences.

1. ⓜom goes to ⓢandy ⓟoint ⓑeach.

   ⓘ go to ⓢandy ⓟoint ⓑeach.
   _____

   Mom and I go to Sandy Point Beach

2. ⓘ take a pail.

   ⓘ take a scoop.
   _____

   I take a pail and scoop.

3. See ⓓad help us build our house.

   See ⓛeon help us build our house.
   _____

   See Dad and Leon help us build our house.

At Home: Draw a picture of your dream playhouse. Give it a special name. Write a sentence about it.

Sand Castle • **Book 1.5/Unit 6** (149)

© Macmillan/McGraw-Hill

Name_____

Make one sentence from each pair of sentences.
Write the new sentence.

1. Dad has wood.

   Dad has a bucket of nails.

   _____

   Dad has wood and a bucket of nails.

2. The boys want to help.

   I want to help.

   _____

   The boys and I want to help.

3. We work hard.

   We finish the house.

   _____

   We work hard and finish the house.

4. Soon, winter will be here.

   Soon, snowy days will be here.

   _____

   Soon, winter and snowy days will be here.

5. Our new house is warm.

   Our new house is cozy.

   _____

   Our new house is warm and cozy.

At Home: Review this page together.

© Macmillan/McGraw-Hill